THE FLUTE

THE FLUTE

Ken Wilson-Max
Catell Ronca

TINY OWL

This is the flute

It sounds like colour

It sounds like yellow

Easy and mellow...

Or bright
like the sun

It whispers sweet secrets

Then blows
like cold,
grey wind

It's a
bright pink
scream!

And a lilac sigh

Floating
like a
butterfly

The flute is poetry

Play your flute!